Wipe-clean
Times Tables

9 × 2 =

10 × 2 =

- Supports Maths in schools
- Notes and tips for grown-ups
- Wipe clean for endless practice

Here are some of the woodland animals you'll meet in this book. They are learning about the 2, 5 and 10 times tables.

Squilly the squirrel

Foxy the fox

2 groups of 5 butterflies

Hug the bear

Stripe the badger

2 lines of 3

3 lines of 2

Coco the raccoon

Bun the rabbit

You can use the pen to help the animals with their calculations. Draw over the dotted lines and write the numbers in the boxes.

USBORNE KEY SKILLS

Wipe-clean
Times Tables

Illustrated by Maddie Frost

Written by Holly Bathie
Designed by Maddison Warnes

Mo the mouse

Moley the mole

Spike the hedgehog

Olly the owl

There are answers, and notes for grown-ups at the back of the book.

Edited by Jessica Greenwell
Series Editor: Felicity Brooks

Groups of 2

Spike and his friend are taking a walk. Trace the numbers in the boxes below the picture.

| 1 | group of | 2 | animals | = | 2 | animals altogether |

Two of their friends come to join them. Trace the numbers and write the total in the boxes.

| 2 | groups of | 2 | animals | = | | animals altogether |

1 2 3 4 5 6 7 8 9 10

Another two friends come to join the walk. Trace the numbers and write in the boxes below the picture.

4

2 more

Help Moley with her butterfly spotting by tracing the numbers and filling in the empty boxes. You could draw a ring around each group of 2 butterflies as you count them.

4 x 2 butterflies = ☐ butterflies

5 x 2 butterflies = ☐ butterflies

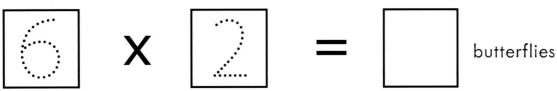

Now draw 2 more butterflies and complete this calculation.

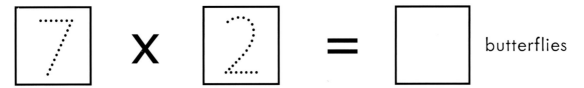

Now draw 2 more butterflies and write the new calculation.

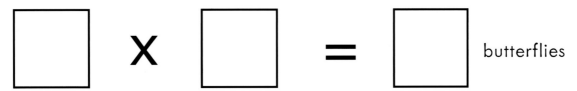

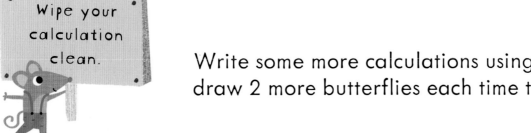

Write some more calculations using 2. You could draw 2 more butterflies each time to help you.

Multiplying with 2

Stripe and Squilly are collecting cherries and need help to complete their calculations. Trace the numbers and fill in the empty boxes.

$$9 \times 2 = \boxed{}$$

$$10 \times 2 = \boxed{}$$

Now Stripe and Squilly are collecting acorns. They have arranged them neatly to see who has more. Complete the calculations to find out.

Do I have more than you?

Stripe has 2 rows of 10 acorns.

2 X 10 = ☐

Squilly has 10 rows of 2 acorns.

10 X 2 = ☐

Squilly and Stripe have exactly the same number of acorns. Whichever order you write a multiplying calculation in, the answer will stay the same.

11 12 13 14 15 16 17 18 19 20

The 2 times table

Groups of 5

When Hug is fishing, he can fit 5 fish each time in his net. Can you trace the fish and finish his calculation for him?

I can see some little red fish!

I can see a big brown bear!

 x  fish =  fish

Count 5 more fish each time to complete these calculations. You could draw another group of 5 fish in the river each time to help you.

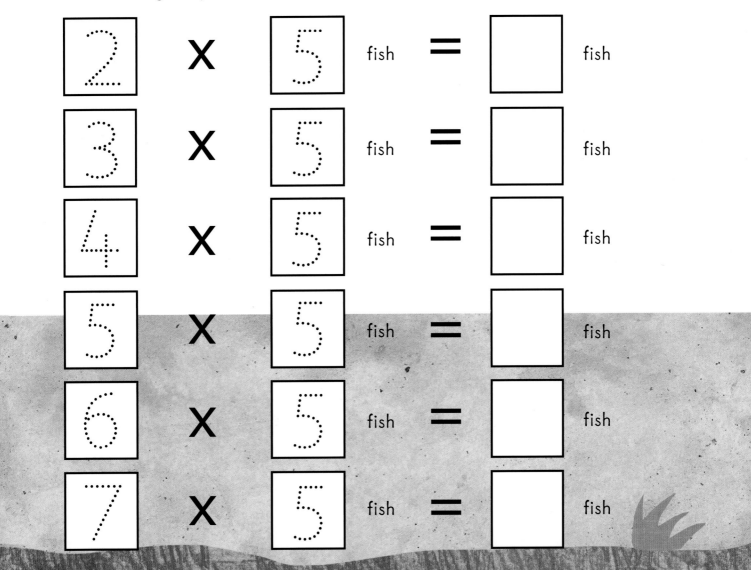

2	X	5	fish	=		fish
3	X	5	fish	=		fish
4	X	5	fish	=		fish
5	X	5	fish	=		fish
6	X	5	fish	=		fish
7	X	5	fish	=		fish

30   35   40   45   50

Multiplying with 5

Help Mo find out how many flowers there are. Draw a ring around a group of 5 flowers. Keep drawing rings around groups of 5 until all the flowers are in groups.

Count the number of groups you have made, then complete the calculation.

Draw 1 more group of 5 flowers, then complete the calculation.

| 5 | 10 | 15 | 20 | 25 |

Draw 9 spots on each bug, then complete the calculation below.

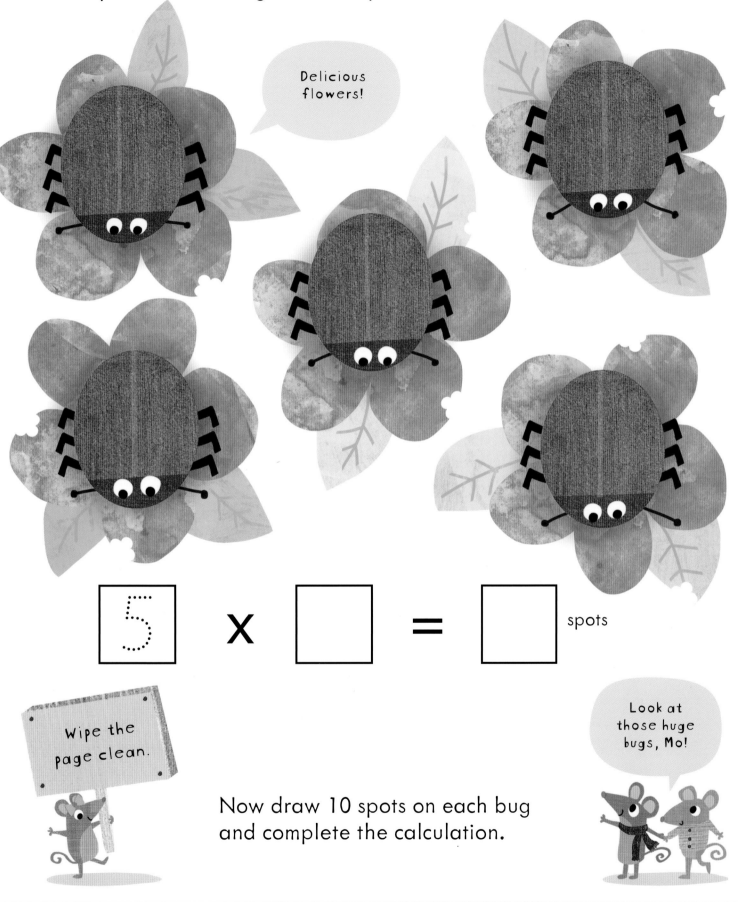

5 X ☐ = ☐ spots

Now draw 10 spots on each bug and complete the calculation.

30   35   40   45   50

14

The 5 times table

Help Foxy finish the 5 times table.

1	X	5	=	5
2	X	5	=	10
3	X	5	=	15
4	X	5	=	
5	X	5	=	
	X	5	=	
	X	5	=	
	X	5	=	
	X	5	=	
	X	5	=	

Hold on tight, Foxy!

5   10   15   20   25

5 X 1 = 5

5 X 2 = 10

5 X 3 = 15

5 X 4 =

5 X 5 =

5 X ☐ =

5 X ☐ =

5 X ☐ =

5 X ☐ =

5 X ☐ =

Can you spot a pattern that helps you to fill in the numbers in the blue boxes?

Check the answers on page 25 to see if you were right.

Rows of 10

Draw more rows of 10 vegetables to fill Bun's vegetable patch.
At the end of each row, write how many vegetables there are in total.

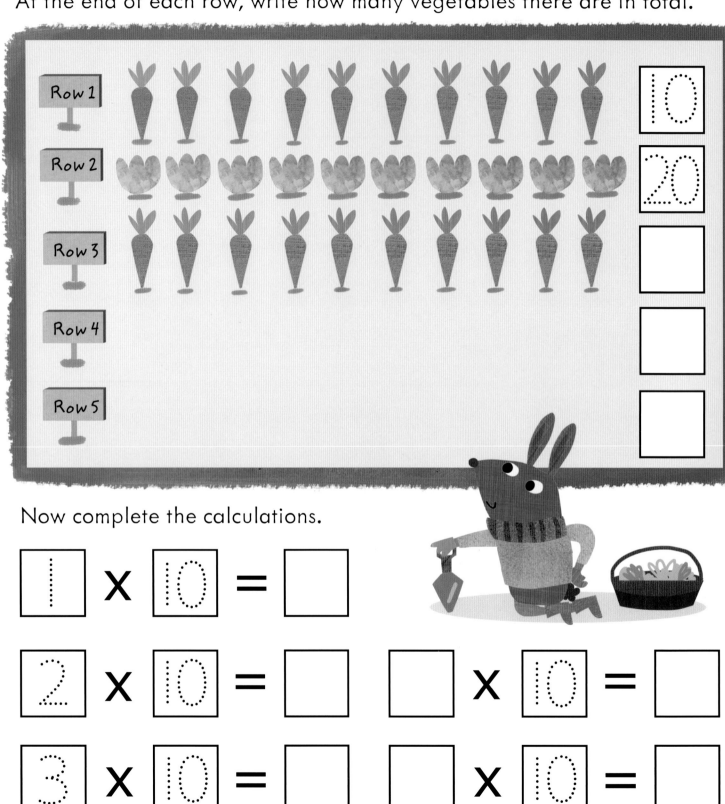

Row 1   10

Row 2   20

Row 3

Row 4

Row 5

Now complete the calculations.

$$1 \times 10 = \boxed{}$$

$$2 \times 10 = \boxed{} \qquad \boxed{} \times 10 = \boxed{}$$

$$3 \times 10 = \boxed{} \qquad \boxed{} \times 10 = \boxed{}$$

10   20   30   40   50

Multiplying with 10

There are 10 vegetables in each of Mo's crates.
Complete the calculation to find out how many
vegetables there are in total.

Fresh veg
for sale!

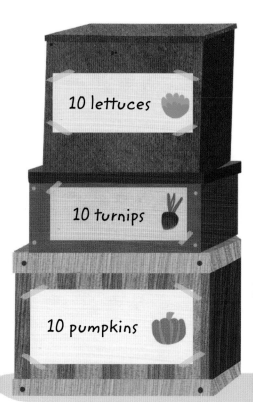

10 lettuces

10 turnips

10 pumpkins

10 cucumbers

10 potatoes

10 carrots

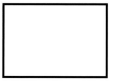 X  =

vegetables at the
market today.

Wipe the
calculation
clean.

Now draw 1 more crate of 10 vegetables
and complete the calculation.

Wipe the calculation clean again and write
other calculations using 10. You could draw
some more crates to help you.

The 10 times table

Can you help Squilly finish the 10 times table?

1	X	10	=	10
2	X	10	=	20
3	X	10	=	
	X		=	
	X		=	
	X		=	
	X		=	
	X		=	
	X		=	
10	X	10	=	100

The 10 times table goes all the way to 100!

| 10 | 20 | 30 | 40 | 50 |

10 X 1 = 10

10 X 2 = 20

10 X 3 =

☐ X ☐ =

☐ X ☐ =

☐ X ☐ =

☐ X ☐ =

☐ X ☐ =

☐ X ☐ =

10 X 10 = 100

Can you help me fill in my table?

The numbers in the blue boxes are in the **10** times table.

100 square

You can use this '100 square' to look at all the numbers in the 2, 5 and 10 times tables.

Help me by drawing a circle around the rest of the numbers in the 2 times table.

1	②	3	④	5	⑥	7	8	9	10
11	12	13	14	15	16	17	18	19	20
21	22	23	24	25	26	27	28	29	30
31	32	33	34	35	36	37	38	39	40
41	42	43	44	45	46	47	48	49	50
51	52	53	54	55	56	57	58	59	60
61	62	63	64	65	66	67	68	69	70
71	72	73	74	75	76	77	78	79	80
81	82	83	84	85	86	87	88	89	90
91	92	93	94	95	96	97	98	99	100

Can you spot all the numbers in the 5 times table? Draw a square around each one.

Then draw a triangle around all the numbers in the 10 times table.

Times table calculations

Help the animals complete these 2, 5 and 10 times table calculations.

See if you can write some more calculations here...

...then wipe them clean and write some more.

Times tables quiz

Find out how much you can remember about the 2, 5 and 10 times tables by doing this quiz. Answers on page 24.

A. Coco and Spike need help sorting out these numbers. Write each number in the correct circle.

75   32   45

68   25   15   12

6

96   8

My circle is for numbers in the 2 times table.

My circle is for numbers in the 5 times table.

2 times table

5 times table

B. Can you think of more numbers in the 10 times table for Hug?

Write all the ones that are more than 10 but less than 100 in his circle.

10

100

10 times table

C. Has Moley got all of her calculations right? Put a
tick in the box next to the ones that are correct.

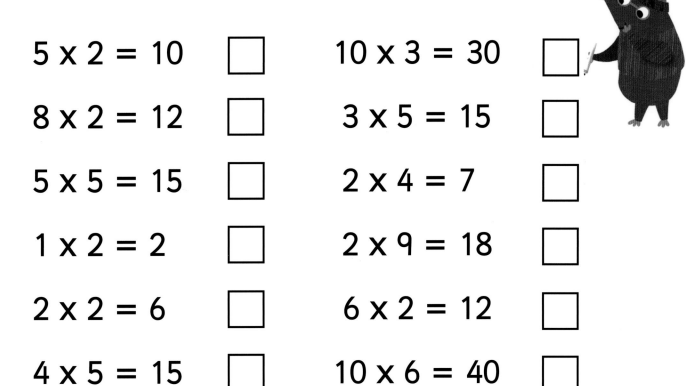

5 x 2 = 10 ☐   10 x 3 = 30 ☐

8 x 2 = 12 ☐   3 x 5 = 15 ☐

5 x 5 = 15 ☐   2 x 4 = 7 ☐

1 x 2 = 2 ☐   2 x 9 = 18 ☐

2 x 2 = 6 ☐   6 x 2 = 12 ☐

4 x 5 = 15 ☐   10 x 6 = 40 ☐

D. Copy the calculations Moley got wrong into
the blank spaces below, and this time write
the correct answers for her.

E. Complete these calculations for Foxy and Bun.

9 x 10 = ☐

8 x 5 = ☐

5 x 2 = ☐

10 x 9 = ☐

6 x 5 = ☐

4 x 5 = ☐

7 x 10 = ☐

3 x 2 = ☐

7 x 1 = ☐

2 x 8 = ☐

9 x 2 = ☐

1 x 10 = ☐

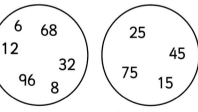

Quiz answers

A.

6   68
12
96   32
8

25
45
75   15

B.

10   20
30   40   50
60   70   80
90   100

C. These are the ones Moley got right:

5 x 2 = 10   3 x 5 = 15

1 x 2 = 2   2 x 9 = 18

10 x 3 = 30   6 x 2 = 12

D. 8 x 2 = 16   4 x 5 = 20

5 x 5 = 25   2 x 4 = 8

2 x 2 = 4   10 x 6 = 60

E. 9 x 10 = 90   6 x 5 = 30   7 x 1 = 7

8 x 5 = 40   4 x 5 = 20   2 x 8 = 16

5 x 2 = 10   7 x 10 = 70   9 x 2 = 18

10 x 9 = 90   3 x 2 = 6   1 x 10 = 10

Score 1 point for each correct answer and write your score in this box:
If you want to get a higher score, wipe the pages clean and try again.

☐
42